Scary Larry

Story and pictures by Bob Reese

ARC
** ROCKFO

D1104068

MY 30 WORDS ARE:

grasshopper	is	said
hop	very	Papa
in	scary	drop
the	and	a
sand	mean	rock
stay	hairy	on
away	what	head
from	can	out
Larry	we	miss
land	do	sandy

Library of Congress Cataloging in Publication Data
Reese, Bob.
    Scary Larry (the very very hairy tarantula): story and pictures.
    (Captain Critter Reader)
    Summary: Papa Grasshopper attempts to protect
the other grasshoppers from a scary hairy tarantula.
    [1.   Grasshopper, Tarantulas – Fiction.   2.   Stories in rhyme]
I. Title.   II.   Series.
ISBN 0-89868-556-7 – Library Bound
ISBN 0-89868-557-5 – Soft Bound

Grasshoppers hopping

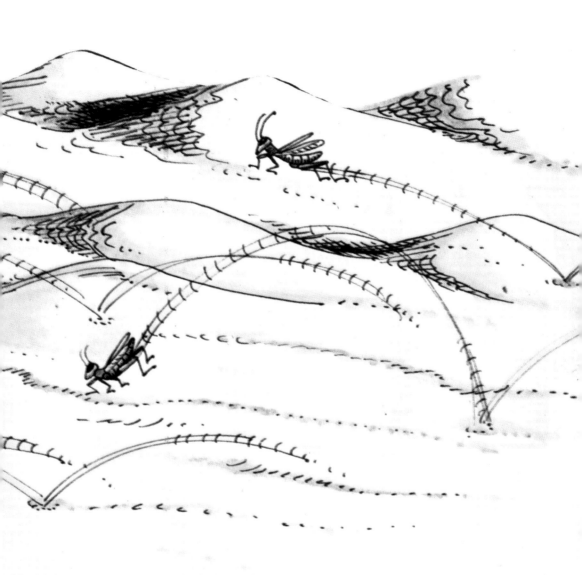

in the sandy sand,

stay away from

Larry's land.

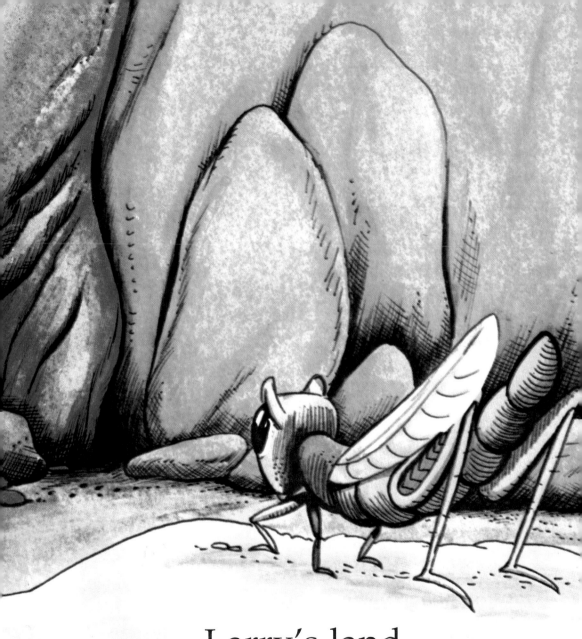

Larry's land

is very scary,

and Larry is

very mean and hairy

"What can we do?"

the grasshoppers said.

"Papa can drop a rock

on Scary Larry's head."

Larry hopped out,

very mean and hairy

Papa dropped the rock

and missed Scary Larry.

"Stay away, stay away, stay away!" Larry said.

Papa hopped on
Scary Larry's head.

Papa said, "Stay away
from grasshopper land,

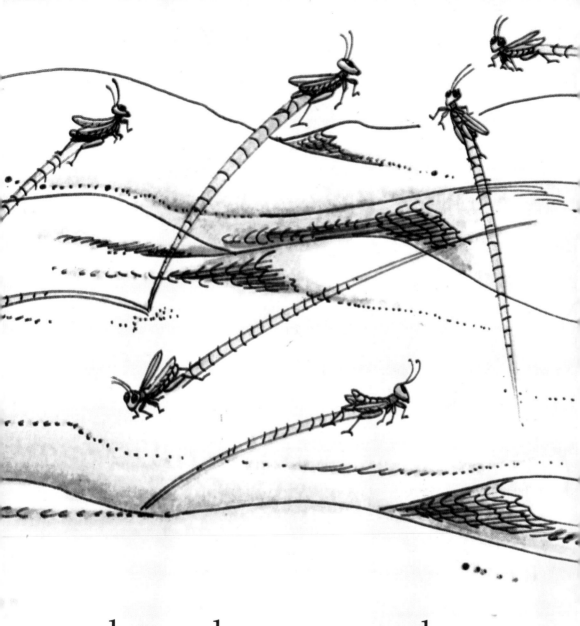

and grasshoppers can hop
in the sandy sand."

Bob Reese

Story teller, writer and artist, Bob Reese has written and illustrated over 100 books for beginning readers.

Bob Reese was born in 1938 in Hollywood, California. His mother Isabelle was an English teacher in the Los Angeles city Schools.

After his graduation from high school he went to work for Walt Disney Studios as an animation cartoonist. He received his B.S. degree in Art and Business and began work as a freelance illustrator and designer.